HIGH HERITAGE

HIGH HERITAGE

Poems of Wales

by

A. G. PRYS-JONES

CHRISTOPHER DAVIES
Llandybie   Carmarthenshire

First Published in mcmlxix
by Christopher Davies (Publishers) Limited
Swansea and Llandybie
Printed in Wales
by Merlin Press
Llandybie
All rights reserved

Dedicated to the youth of Wales,

and especially to

Laura, Kate, Timothy, Matthew and Lucy

Contents

Foreword

By Sir Ben Bowen Thomas, M.A., LL.D., Fellow of Jesus College, Oxford; President, University College of Wales, Aberystwyth, and of the National Institute of Adult Education. Former Permanent Secretary of the Welsh Department, Ministry of Education, and Chairman, Executive Board, Unesco.

My father first introduced me to A. G. Prys-Jones, that is to his English poems as they appeared in *"The Welsh Outlook"* many years ago. They gave both of us much pleasure, and I remember that when my father was packed off to a convalescent home after one of his too frequent bouts of illness, one of the books he took with him for his comfort was *"Poems of Wales"* by A. G. Prys-Jones, published in 1923 by Basil Blackwell, Oxford. He would have been delighted to find that there is still song in this poet's heart in 1968.

In the course of the years, it was my good fortune to be numbered with the poet's friends and colleagues, to know his concern for the welfare of Wales generally, and to share in his devotion to her school children particularly. Here, as an Inspector of Schools, he made an abiding contribution in the Owen M. Edwards tradition, inspiring teachers and children alike, as much by his learning and personal charm as by his felicitous writing in prose and poetry.

I am glad that he has assembled this further collection of poems for our pleasure. His immediate concern is for the children in the upper classes of our primary schools and in the lower forms of our secondary schools. Nearly all the poems are Welsh in content: a few are adapted from Welsh poetry: all are intelligible and avowedly "romantic" in period. Children will enjoy them all, and we, the elders will find them refreshing. I greet old friends like "St. Govan" and "Dick Fisherman" with special cordiality. But I miss one or two others, in particular, "To Valeria, a Roman lady buried at Caerleon during the Roman occupation of Britain." I have always been an admirer of hers, because she chose the banks of the Usk rather than the Tiber, and golden Gwent rather than mighty Rome to be her resting place.

Ben Bowen Thomas.

Author's Note

In view of Sir Ben's admiration for "Valeria" I have much pleasure in resuscitating my early commemoration of her. So the lady is now honourably included among these verses.

Most of these pieces have previously appeared from time to time in various Welsh and English newspapers, periodicals and anthologies over the past half century. Some, now in revised form herein, were also included in my two little volumes, *"Poems of Wales"* (Basil Blackwell, Oxford, 1923) and *"Green Places"* (Gwasg Aberystwyth, 1948.) both long out of print. A number have been broadcast in radio programmes from Wales, and several were set to music by Welsh, English and American composers and published as songs.

The present volume is intended primarily as a collection of verse, predominantly about Wales, for individual and choral speaking by pupils in Welsh schools. It is hoped that the poems may pass the critical test of being read aloud, and prove attractive in content. For the most part they are simple in style and romantic in spirit. Such an unfashionable approach may perhaps not be unacceptable to older readers who still find themselves perplexed, and their enjoyment inhibited by the obscurity, sophistication, obsessive introspection and experimental eccentricity of "advanced" modern verse, all of which are by-products of the revolt against traditionalism. Identification with the serious malaise of contemporary society has tended to replace sentiment by satire, emotion by cynicism, imagination by bleak or sordid realism, and true compassion by cruel irony. Fortunately, it is abundantly clear that these characteristics are very rarely to be found in the work of Anglo-Welsh poets who are writing today.

It is also hoped that these verses may help to awaken interest in our history and to enhance affection for our native land.

Roman Road

This is the way the Romans came,
Steadily, steadily over the hill:
This is the way the Romans came
(And if you listen, you'll hear them still!)
Men from Italy, Africa, Gaul,
Resolute soldiers, strong and tall,
Rome the mother of one and all
Sent them to work her will.

Cohorts, cohorts, with breasts of flame,
(Straight as an arrow-flight over the hill!)
This is the way the Romans came
To build and govern, to sow and till:
Men from Asia, Germany, Spain,
Marching along in sun and rain,
(Forests to fell and fens to drain
And Britons to tame and drill!)

Euphrates, Danube and Nile and Rhine,
(The eagles have drunk their fill!)
Thames and Severn and Forth and Tyne,
(Caerleon just over the hill!)
And this is the way the Romans went,
Their glory fading, their vigour spent,
Over the rolling downs of Gwent,
(Steadily over the hill!)

The road they fashioned pays homage yet
To a splendour that long lies still:
And we that follow must not forget
The Roman courage, the Roman will:
And dreamers hear when the shadows fall
The stirring sounds of their bugle-call,
(Men of the Empire, Romans all,
Marching over the hill!)

[9]

The Mountains of Glamorgan

The mountains of Glamorgan
Look down towards the sea,
Their song comes clearer than a bell
On southern winds that sink and swell,
And there they stands to sentinel
A vale of history.

And when they wear the beauty
And the mystery of Spring
Maybe our dead folk gather there
To bless the land they loved, in prayer,
For glens and woodlands everywhere
Are loud with whispering.

So when my years have fallen
Like sere leaves from a tree,
I know that I shall yearn to go
And wander with them to and fro
Along those singing hills I know
That look towards the sea.

Welsh Manor Garden

A house of lovely windows,
Diamond-paned, half-opened:
The slender gleam of candles
Playing on smooth, dark tables,
And straying
In small, white fingers to high wainscots
Where grave ancestral portraits
Move heads and limbs in mime
Slowly to frail candle-rhyme.

In the rustling dusk
The night-winds wake and wander
Through coloured woodlands
Rippling the fishponds
With many questions:
The lily-blossoms sigh for answers,
But the tall oaks, the glossy beeches,
Ample and old, so very old, remember
The satined, swaying dancers,
The thrill-winged violins;
And after,
The vivid, dark-haired poets, the poignant harpers,
The folk-songs, and the laughter.

What moved across the lawns?
Only the moonlight
Troubling the patterned swards, the shorn yew-hedges
With ghosts of memories.
Within the enchanted house
Now still, and silver-islanded
By the high tides of the young moon,
The miming portraits fall on sleep again,
And fluttering moths like dim, dissolving dreams
Wheel back to silent gardens
Where only the trees remember
The beautiful young faces.

The Secret People

Tall Kings, tawny-bearded,
And Queens whom love has kissed,
Come walking through the woodlands,
Amid the blue-bell mist.

And ships with scarlet cordage,
With towers as high as noon,
Sail in these silent spaces
Beneath the silent moon.

These are the secret people
Who sleep behind the veil
Of the sunrise and the moonrise
In the star-light of a tale.

These are the vanished people
Who are our kith and kin
When the world's great tides are falling
And the heart's swift tides come in.

They bring blue days for singing,
They give white hours for prayer,
And scatter gifts like blossoms
On this soft midnight air:

Words that are as sweet as honey
And dreams as strong as time,
And tiny songs so delicate
That will not walk in rhyme.

Snowdrops

(From the Welsh of Cynan's "Eirlysiau")

I heard no trumpet sounding
Through Winter's sombre tomb,
Or noise of angels rolling
Grim headstones;
In my room
I slept as deeply unconcerned
As Pilate, when there died,
After His base betrayal,
The One they crucified:
But Spring's gay resurrection
Stirred all the country-side.
For when I woke at daybreak
And looked towards the moor,
Behold, a thousand snowdrops
Were crowding at my door . . .
"All in their gleaming raiment,
White as the crested wave,
And glorious like their Master
New-risen from the grave."

Saint Govan

Saint Govan, the hermit, built a cell
By the side of the Pembroke sea:
And there, as the crannied sea-gulls dwell,
In his tiny, rock-bound citadel
He mused on eternity.

And when he had tolled his lonely bell
He would pause from his prayers to see
The sunsets redden the rolling swell,
And glimpse the beauty that cast its spell
On the land where he loved to be.

And so, with joy, in his hidden cell
He lived till his soul sped free:
And one may wonder, and who can tell,
If good Saint Govan likes Heaven as well
As his cell by the Pembroke sea.

On a Welsh Soldier of Fortune

Because, one Spring, some new, disturbing star
Thrust in his lusty blood a fiery lance,
He took his prowess to strange lands afar,
Selling his sword from Muscovy to France.

His skill, his valour, his rewards were high,
He rode with princes, battled with the strong,
But always, as the alien years went by,
Kept hold upon his mountain speech and song.

In courts and camps and sieges he retold
With native eloquence the lore of Wales,
Of Catraeth's epic heroes and the old,
Bright magic of the Mabynogion tales.

At last, deep-scarred, but now with wealth to share
Among his kinsfolk on Eryri's side,
He boarded ship at La Rochelle, but there,
Smitten by sudden fever, burned and died.

Through Yuletide seas, all white and winter-blown,
His faithful comrades brought their captain back
To the wild uplands which had called him home,
Marching on Roman road and ridgeway track.

They bore him gently on a rough-hewn bier
By glens where once his hunting hawks flew high,
To lonely moorlands where in tier on tier
The mountains rise majestic to the sky.

At night they laid him in a tomb of stone
And gathered round his cairn in torch-light flame:
And there an old, blind minstrel he had known
Plucked at a plaintive harp and sang his fame.

Wil Huws

Wil Huws the village sexton
Was three score years and ten:
He'd buried far more people
Than he ever saw again:
Three hundred he had laid to rest
With a proper craftsman's pride,
There wasn't a better sexton
In all the countryside.

Wil Huws had filled the churchyard
So neatly and so full
That an adjoining field was bought
From the landlord of "The Bull":
But Wil, in his ripe wisdom,
Had kept one church plot free,
"I'll soon be joining up" he said,
"So here's the place for me."

"For fifty years I've tended them,
The place is like a park,
And everything's been quiet here,
No hauntings after dark:
While most were decent, tidy folk,
Others were bad and bold,
But, in fair-play, I'm bound to say
They've all been good as gold.

With poachers, squires and farmers
There's always just a risk
That a few of the noisy, wild ones
Might feel inclined to frisk:
But the parsons and the pastors here
No doubt had influence too,
Though if I'm buried somewhere else
Lord knows what they will do!"

Wil Huws, the village sexton
Was a man who kept his word:
I'm sure he's perched in the yew-tree now
Like a wise, old, watchful bird,
With an eagle-eye fixed on the lot of them
Marking them grave by grave,
And a special look at the squires perhaps
To see that *they* behave.

Some day Archangel Gabriel
Will call them unawares,
The good ones and the bad ones
The white wheat and the tares:
And if I could be there then
And clear of my own affairs,
I'd give a lot to see old Wil
Marching them up the stairs.

Gwalchmai's Delight

(Freely adapted from the Welsh of Gwalchmai ap Meilyr, a 12th century court poet.)

Early over the eastern marches
The sun's first envoys come
Bearing the banners of daybreak,
Behind them the stripling Summer rides
Gay in the garments of May:
Sweet to my ears
Is the babble of birds
In the bright, blue air of morning.

Golden my ornate corslet,
Bold my heart,
Before the host there is no lion braver,
No lightning like my onset.

At night I have kept close vigil,
Shielding the shallow ford
Of the whispering waters of Dygen Freiddin:
Very green is the virgin grass,
Crystal the river,
And the soaring song of the nightingale
Is an ode which has no ending.

A Song of the Pilgrim Road

The road to old Saint David's
Is the white road of the blest,
The roving road which gave the vales
The pilgrims' songs, the palmers' tales,
When all the wandering roads of Wales
Went winding to the west.

The road to old Saint David's
Is a road of hills and sea,
A road where prelates,lords and kings,
With peasants, chiefs and princelings
Came humbly bearing offerings
To a cherished sanctuary.

The road to old Saint David's,
As famed as the road to Rome,
Leads to the lonely, hidden place
Where David raised his house of grace,
And here the heart of an ancient race
Found an abiding home.

The road to old Saint David's
Is the road of the saint who trod
Its first rough trackways to proclaim
The love of Christ, and lit the flame
Of faith that glories in the Name
And Fatherhood of God.

The road to old Saint David's
Through all its fabled ways
Remembers how from age to age
Men came on pious pilgrimage
Seeking a nation's heritage,
And singing their songs of praise.

A Ballad of Owain Glyn Dŵr's Rising

(September, 1400.)

My son, the mist is clearing and the moon will soon be high,
And then we'll hear the thudding hooves, the horsemen speeding
by,
With murmurs coming nearer, carried over on the breeze,
Of the men who march in secret through the cloisters of the trees:
Tonight we two go riding, for the threads of fate are spun,
And we join Glyn Dŵr at Corwen at the rising of the sun.

For yesterday our leader was proclaimed the Prince of Wales,
His call to arms is sounding now among the hills and vales,
And Owain, heir of dynasties, in this auspicious year
May be our great deliverer, foretold by bard and seer:
And rumour runs that Arthur's voice is heard along the west
Acclaiming this descendant of Cadwaladr the Blest.

At last shall I unsheath again my father's two-edged sword,
And hand you mine to strike amain at Ruthin's tyrant lord,
Because I've waited, waited long throughout the bitter years
For this hour of freedom's challenge and the flashing of the spears:
So now we two must face as one the hazards of the night
To pledge our lives to Owain at the breaking of the light.

My son, go kiss your mother, kiss her gently, she'll not wake,
For an older mother calls you, though you perish for her sake:
The fabled Dragon banner flies once more above the Dee
Where the sons of Wales are gathering to set our people free
From wrong and dire oppression: pray, my son for strength anew,
For widows will be weeping at the falling of the dew.

Dick Fisherman

(On Teifi-side.)

Old Dick Fisherman
Is happier than the squire,
Wiser than the minister
Studying by his fire:
Squire goes a-hunting
And parson's deep in books,
But old Dick Fisherman
Learns from woods and brooks.

Old Dick Fisherman
Has kind and gentle eyes,
He tends all wounded creatures
And listens for their cries:
He's never had much money,
And has never worn fine clothes,
But his roving realm holds secrets
That only Dick knows.

Once I wandered with him
To hear the songs he weaves
Walking in the woodlands
At the falling of the leaves:
And once I glimpsed the welcome
That Dick so often sees
In the greetings of the rivers
And the friendship of the trees.

There'll be brown pools in Paradise
Beyond the last star,
For the Lord makes due provision
For all the sorts that are:
And it's there by woods and waters
That I may hear again
Old Dick Fisherman
Singing in the rain.

Winter Woods
(Carmarthenshire.)

Low are the lamps of Autumn,
And the woods
Bereaved and barren on the gusty hills
Stand gaunt, like plundered towns, along
These wind-swept solitudes.
So soon
Their tawny gold is scattered:
And the moon
That lovely Queen
Of all things cold and comfortless
Has seen
Their glory wrenched, their tall, defiant
Torches quenched
In the wind's grey eloquence.
And so
In recompense
She casts her silver nets of light
About their thin, bare boughs at night
Giving them beauty new and strange
And starry-bright,
And thus illumed
With other harmonies
They do not fear
The sounding hosts of Winter drawing near.

But the red squirrel
In his snug retreat
Beyond the cold
Of the frost's keen fingers thrusting there,
Sleeps on and dreams
In his warm-bedded lair
Of all the rifled, shining gold
He saw along the drifted wold:
And hears no drums,
Nor the long beat
Of Winter's legions thundering by
On iron feet.

Night in Snowdonia

Here on the quiet shores of Gwynant Lake
The tumults of the tragic years are stilled,
While these ancestral mountains swiftly take
Captive my pilgrim heart, my quest fulfilled
In awe and wonder: thus, entranced, I hear
Along the passes, through the sounding glen,
Their timeless challenge, steadfast and austere,
And know Llywelyn musters with his men
Like wraiths above the cloud-rack, eagle-high
In proud Eryri where his sentries call
Their comrades down the ramparts of the sky:
But in the south the stars of destiny fall
On fatal Irfon Bridge to herald years
Of bitter conquest, tyranny and tears.

Viroconium

(Wroxeter on the Severn. Roman fortress and tribal centre of the British Kingdom of the Cornovii. Sacked by the invading Saxons.)

The Saxons from the midlands swooped and ravaged,
The yellow plague sped with them from the east:
And now the granaries, once high with harvest,
Hold not a grain for famished man or beast.

No watchman walks upon the tumbled turret,
No sentinel along the crumbled wall,
Nothing is left that anyone could covet,
No maid, no chattel nor an ox in stall.

Charred beams lie black and broken in the markets,
Forsaken hearths are cold and dumb with dust,
The toppled temples filled with fallen rubble,
The marble crusted with the rain's red rust.

Here nothing stirs: the slain lie deep in silence
Where murrain rides the dark, miasmal ground:
But in the mist a withered host awakens
And moves towards the hills without a sound.

Evening at St. Fagans

Here in these meadows angry men made war
Marring the Vale with blood and death and fire,
Where now the corn grows tall for harvest-tide
And cattle move at ease to their cool byre:
Along the fields the scarlet poppies glow
Like cressets at the burials of kings,
And from the blossomed belfry of the briar
A blithe and solitary song-thrush sings.

Gone are the blazoned standards: in their stead
The high madonna lilies shine like stars
Where once there gleamed the morions and the swords
Of bearded captains tempered in hot wars:
And through the mullioned windows where there flowed
The tuck of kettle-drums at morning light,
The tides of evening pass, deep-drenched with rose
And all the perfumes of the summer night.

To Valeria

(A young Roman lady buried at Caerleon during the Roman
occupation of Britain.)

How came you to this misty, northern isle
Your Empire's frontier, set amid the foam
Of turbulent winter seas, so far from home,
Where under kindlier skies the sun-god's smile
Ripened your beauty to its radiant hour?
What bonds of love and duty had the power
To draw you from your land of warm delight
In youthful ardour, and with eyes more bright
Than almond-blossom blown on springtide air:
What other cords had failed to keep you there?

Sometimes I see you drooping, see you age
And languish like some brilliant-plumaged bird
Stolen from tropic glades, which says no word
But stares and starves bewildered in a cage:
Valeria, did you sigh and weep and pine
For Tiber and the purple-clustered vine,
The oleander's hues and the rich blue
Of southern seas that summer skies fall through?
Concealing grief beneath your Roman pride,
Could it be thus, Valeria, that you died?

I like to think that long before you went
Into the silence which knows no recall,
You found new happiness which held you thrall
Along these hills and vales of golden Gwent:
And while you walked beside the winding Usk
You saw the fairy folk who dance at dusk,
And heard old melodies upon the air
Plucked from their harps by wandering minstrels there,
And braver music from a prophet's hands
Whose voice declaimed his dreams of wondrous things,
Of people countless as the Tiber's sands

Arising from these shadowy forest-lands,
With great sea-captains, conquerors and kings,
And poets with their winged imaginings,
And teeming cities, miracles to come
When Rome, your mighty mother would be dumb.

Perhaps the changeful beauty of this land
Enchanted you, and as its welcomed guest
You came to love, and then to understand
The brooding mystery of the ancient west:
And songs more poignant than the songs of Italy
Took seisin of your heart and held it true,
So that if ever it were offered you
To live beside the blue Tyrrhenian sea
That moves in silken murmurs tidelessly,
You would have chosen this dear isle again,
This isle, these mountains and the healing rain.

Spring Comes to Glamorgan

Today I saw Spring's footprints in the Vale,
Small snowdrops glistening in a dawn-green dell
Beyond Llysworney:
And then, towards the sea,
Below St. Hilary, where thrush-songs rings,
I heard her trysting-call fall through the trees
Within the primrose wood where Merlin flings
His saffron mantle to the daffodils.

Today, I saw grey tombstones hoar with moss
In deep St. Donat's where the Stradlings sleep
Between their rock-fast castle-keep
And the soft lowland.
And there I saw the carven Crucified
Upon His Calvary Cross:
He did not stir, for all His suffering;
Nor moved the marble angels from their places
To quench His endless agony.

But they that lay so long with upturned faces,
Each in his narrow niche of this rich earth
Within the sanctuary of the lichened wall,
These all
Had heard Spring's call,
And woken from their oaken sleeping.
And so they pass
Along the old, familiar pathways of the grass
Towards the woods where birds are music-making,
Where crocuses are breaking:
They come, these visitants, with arms outspread;
No bonds of wood and clay
Can keep them captive here on such a day:
On such a day as this along the Vale
There are no dead.

Saint David

Out of fabulous tales
And the legends told
Of Saint David of Wales
In cloister and cell
By those who extolled
His virtue and grace,
We have woven his spell:
And have heard his voice
Like a silver bell
From missal and page
Limned bright with art,
And hallowed with age
He returns to our heart....

With the chorals of Spring
On the wind-blown plain,
And the promise of meadows
Grown rich with rain,
With the earth that exults
In the conquering sun,
And Winter retreating
And blossoms begun;
With daffodils shaking
Their pennons of gold
And woodlands awaking,
He comes to his fold
To grant us his blessing
And the light of his face,
As he came long ago
In the dawn of our race.

The Passing of Owain Glyn Dŵr
(Black Mountains.)

Now fades the twilight from the quiet sky,
On cairn and croft the cloaks of darkness fall,
Home to their eyries the great buzzards fly,
And over dusky pools the curlews call:
And here by twisting bridle-paths at night
Came one all travel-stained and battle-torn
Who paused and listened in his friendless plight
To reapers late among the upland corn,
Prince Owain of the Dee, with weary eyes,
Seeking the hills from glen to winding glen
Where the great moors and forests roll and rise,
The refuge of defeated, broken men,
With hounds of Harry Monmouth in full cry
Loosed from the leash where Prince Llywelyn fell,
And listening, he saw the lowland sky
Glow red with flame, and heard his passing-bell.

And here, men say, he vanished in the dawn
Leaving no sign save a wide-open door,
His baldric and his naked sword forlorn
In some deserted hut below the moor,
Where comforted by mourning rain that wept
For his doomed cause, and lulled by sighing trees,
Through these, his darkest hours, he lay and slept:
And then, awakened by the mountain breeze
He rose and shook aside his poignant pain
And strode away unarmed, still proud and brave:
But no one heard his hero-voice again,
And no man knows where lies his lonely grave.

Henry Morgan's March on Panama

Morgan's hair is matted,
His lips are cracked and dry,
His tawny beard is tangled
And his plumed hat hangs awry:
But his voice still booms like thunder
Through the steaming jungle glade
As he marches, bold as Lucifer,
Leading his gaunt brigade.

Twelve hundred famished buccaneers,
Bitten, blistered and bled,
A sweltering mob, accursed and flayed
By the fierce sun overhead:
Twelve hundred starving scarecrows
With hardly a crust to eat,
And only sips from festering pools
In that grim, monstrous heat.

Twelve hundred tortured musketeers
Creeping through clogging mud
Where the reek of rotting mangroves
Wakes havoc in their blood:
Twelve hundred worn-out wretches
Fevered and almost dead,
But Morgan's fiery eloquence
Rallies them on ahead.

Twelve hundred tatterdemalions,
The sorriest, maddest crew
That ever the green savannahs saw
When the Spanish bugles blew:
Twelve hundred struggling skeletons
Who sprang to life and then
In one wild wave took Panama,
For they were Morgan's men.

A Lot to Break

(Ar Y Berwyn.)

I saw him where two mountain roads
Meet at a moorland place,
A labourer breaking heavy stones
With slow and native grace:
And as he worked, the little chips
Went rhyming round his face.

He paused awhile, his hammer poised,
And I, with time to take,
Talked of the marvel of the moor
And the splendour of the lake:
"I must be getting on" he said,
"There's still a lot to break."

Glimpsing That Other Kingdom
(Teifi Valley.)

Lo! here it lies
Close, close at hand
That other kingdom
Once so faint and far:
With these same luminous, western skies,
These eager, probing winds
That filch and fling
All Autumn's golden coinage from the trees:
These bronze and orange woodlands
Bright and quick with tapestries:
These same deep pools of moonlight
And the same high wizardry
Of one white, singing star.

Another new, transfigured land
Of old, familiar sights and sounds
Where time in ceaseless, rhythmic rounds
Brings orchard aisles, and garnered sheaves,
And lingering tangs of burning leaves,
And trees where the last song-bird grieves
For Summer's ecstasy, so warm, so fleet;
And rain that falls on cottage panes
With small and sure, incessant feet.

Lo! here it lies
Close, close at hand:
That other kingdom
Once so faint and far:
What drowsy angel drenched with sleep
Forgot his sentinel watch to keep
Along celestial ramparts dim
With red October dusk? To him
Be mortal praise for this brief blame,
For in that hour of gold and flame
He left Heaven's postern-gate ajar.

[33]

Vigil

(Vale of Clwyd.)

In vigil once, I saw the stars
Like some proud legion in the sky
Arrayed along the shining plain,
While their white Queen the moon went by.

Silent she was and very pure,
And pure was all her white domain,
Such radiant majesty it seemed
Not all the earth's black sin could stain.

Too soon dissolved her pageant there,
Her grace and all her glory furled,
For dawn, that fiery horseman, rode
To wake the tumult of the world.

At Bosworth

Cry "Tudor" here and these green fields will swarm
With companies of ghostly fighting men
Who marched from Wales to make a kinsman king:
And when, in desperate onset, the alarm
Of this momentous battle sounds, so then
Shall you see Henry, locked within the ring
Of Richard's furious charges, hard at bay
Under the Dragon standard and the sun
For one grave hour of this prophetic day,
Till wavering Lord Stanley's horsemen ride
Fresh to the fray, and speed the tides that run
To Henry Tudor: Richard, doomed crowned head
Who fought so fiercely but so swiftly died . . . .
Does he still linger with those Cymric dead
Who by an easier path would long have lain
Deep in their rugged hills beneath the rain?

Over the Frosty Moorland

Over the frosty moorland
The moon is riding high,
And out of the wintry silence
The wraiths of Rome come by.

Ghosts of the old Sixth Legion,
Scythian, Parthian, Gaul,
Centurions, Legate, Tribunes,
Marching towards the Wall.

Out of the tumbling shadows
A proud, imperial throng,
Shaking the buried causeway
With the swing of the Legion's song.

Over the frosty moorland
Their road runs arrow-straight
Through the crumbled camp of the mountains
Swift as the sword of fate.

The little dead Picts of the Border
Wake to the echoing tune,
And the Britons mass in the brushwood
Under the burnished moon.

But the Legion marches onward
Where the silver bugles call,
Down winds of the northern frontier
Where Rome still holds the Wall.

In Welsh Uplands

Puw the Ploughman

Above the glowing rowan-trees
A ploughshare rustles slowly through the stubble
Where Puw the ploughman, lean and puckered,
Plods on alone beneath benignant stars,
Breaking the sullen turf tonight because
The rustic lore he lives by prophesies
A spell of mist and clogging rain tomorrow.

His old, white horse, Abednego,
Walks wearily like Puw,
Both wondering how soon
They'll reach the last, long hedge-row,
And stumble home to deep and dreamless sleep.

They have been here for centuries,
The man, the horse, the rustling plough,
Taming these harsh, high hills:
Undaunted mountain trio
United in a true poetic triad,
Deploying skill and strength and craft
Against the wicked whimsies of the weather,
And winning many battles overnight
By native wisdom and unending toil.

Puw and Abednego are both hill-born,
Descendants of those sinewy progenitors
Who fought the foiling elements,
Subdued the soil and fashioned
With cunning their clean furrows
Across these cloudy acres year by year,
Writing the runes of this Cistercian range.

The masters of these hills
Were tough and frugal, silent men,
Though eloquent enough in prayer,
And turning up a poet now and then:
They usually died old and bent
But still unbeaten by life's labours,
And proudly spurning any alien speech.

Cors-y-Gwaed

(Fenland of Blood.)

Heirs to these marshy lowlands
Willows and reeds remain;
This was no place for pasture,
These are no fields for grain.

Yet here in feuding foray
Young peasants fought and died,
Not knowing why their princes
Drew swords that Eastertide
Drenching with blood these acres,
Stagnant, useless and sour,
Acres that never nourished
Cattle nor crops nor flower.

    So Easter after Easter,
    Dumb as the soil and deep,
    Two hundred men of Meirion
    Unshriven, lie asleep.

Symbols, these barren marshes,
Of continents and seas
Wherein our lord and masters
Still cannot live at ease.
Symbols, those men of Meirion,
They learnt, not knowing why,
When rulers ride in anger
Who are the first to die.

Merlin's Hill

Come slowly, softly over this green hill
Where the cool evening air
Is strangely still:
And mark the brooding silence there
Within the bird-forsaken grove
Where leafy ash and oak and beech
Beseech their branches not to stir
Nor welcome sounds of human speech.

Then look below where red rocks bear
Their blood of that stupendous birth
When first their heads came thrusting there
In vast convulsions of the earth:
And now they guard the solitary cave
Where Merlin and his seven magicians sleep,
Once masters of the wind and wave
And mighty Arthur's seers:
Deep, deep in their dark lair
Within this high, green hill
In fitful slumber they fulfil
The penance of their endless years.

Tread softly, make no sound,
Pass the red rocks with fear,
Beware, beware at set of sun
When nothing here is what it seems,
And these dread sleepers turn and fret
Uneasy in their drifting dreams,
For hosting shadows hasten here,
And old enchantments rise and run
About this place, round grove and mound,
This is great Merlin's ground,
He must not waken yet.

In Llantrithyd Church
(Vale of Glamorgan.)

Here lie the Aubreys, lords of the Manor
Four hundred years ago:
They, too, saw Easter come to Glamorgan
In apple-blossom snow:
They saw high Summer's radiance,
And gentle Autumn's glow:
And here they heard the torrent winds
Of Winter come and go:
But now they all lie sleeping
Between nave and altar
In their long, prescriptive row.

Only the church and the crumbled manor
Remember the Aubreys
Four hundred years ago:
These saw them come to christening,
And marriage and Mass
In the Vale's bright beauty:
And these saw them pass
All, solemn and slow,
To their last resting-places
Beyond the green grass,
In the church
Between nave and altar.

But when, in the bounty of Spring,
Tall daffodils blow,
And again when the lamps of the fall
In the woodlands show
And the vespers ring,
So, surely then the crumbled manor stirs
And whispers low
To the grey church walls
"Tell all the sleeping Aubreys

There below . . .
Lest their long slumber palls,
How constantly each gracious season calls
With its gift of rich blossom,
Warmth, colour, swift snow,
In the Vale they loved tenderly
So long ago."
And the walls never falter,
But murmur so
To the tombs between nave and altar:
And I think that the Aubreys know.

At Valle Crucis Abbey

(Llangollen.)

For centuries the kindly grass
Has clothed the Abbey's scattered stones,
And tenderly the twining trees
Have bound the chancel's fractured bones;
Deep-rooted round this ruined house of prayer
The starry hawthorn and the wild, red rose
Perform their faithful ministries, aware
That every Spring along this hidden glen
The angel of the sanctuary comes and goes
Through aisles of blossom nurtured by the dust
Of prince and peasant, poet and chronicler
Devout or wayward who at last
Found benison and burial here.

And I, in this green, hallowed place,
Was drawn within the silence there,
A realm where language, time and space
Dissolved upon the crystal air;
And all the vale leapt bright with sudden change
To beauty more intense than flaring fire,
Shining with symbols rich and rare and strange,
Until in soaring music, sweet and long,
The birds about the broken choir
Poured forth their hymns of praise in ardent song.

The Return of Arthur

Deep in the heart of Morfa
A thousand warriors rest,
Each clad in knightly armour
With his sword upon his breast:
And there in serried ranks they sleep
Awaiting their lord's behest.

Some night in moon-lit splendour
A noble ship will ride
Full-sailed to silent Morfa,
With a fleet of ships beside . . .
King Arthur's host from Avalon
Escorting him home with pride.

Then a thousand men will waken
To pledge him with their lips,
And march with blazoned banners
To the shore-way and the ships:
And the brilliance of their bright array
Will shine to the moon's eclipse.

And the winging winds will bear them
Through fiery sunsets far
To lands of long-lost causes
Where the last adventures are,
And Arthur's triumphs will be sung
By every glittering star.

From the listening shores of Morfa
The sound of their crusade
Will echo on the swinging tides
To the farthest hill and glade:
Then shall the world's grave wounds be healed
And the world's great songs be made.

The Visitants

In the first far glow of the morning
When the earth lay silver and still,
I heard the sound of a trumpet-call
Come echoing over the hill.

There followed a warrior chieftain
As he rode in the days of old,
His armour flashed fire in the sunrise,
And his great shield glimmered with gold.

At the head of a host of horsemen
He was leading his gallant throng,
And as they passed by in the valley
They were singing a marching song . . .

A tune still heard in my childhood,
A melody rendered with tears
By a harper praising a hero
Who had died in the distant years.

Very proudly they rode, like princes
On a splendid and valiant quest,
And they vanished, gleaming and singing
Away to the gates of the west.

Though often I watched there at dawnlight
They never came riding again,
But always my heart will remember
Those horsemen, that stirring refrain.

In the Vale of Glamorgan

Here the adventurous Norman came
To conquer and abide:
He built in stern, enduring stone
The symbols of his pride.

Turret and tower and rounded arch
Along this sea-girt land
Bear silent witness to the strength
Of his imperious hand.

And now, near mossy priory walls
This golden Autumn day
The ploughman on the stubbled fields
Pursues his ancient way . . .

Turning the rich, brown earth anew,
The soil that links them still,
The Norman in his carven tomb,
The ploughman on the hill.

All-Hallows Eve

(Nos Galan Gaeaf.)

On Bala Lake, with strident cry,
In sudden fear the marsh-fowl fly,
And barren branches quake and groan
Along the shores where waters moan
Beneath a dark, foreboding sky:
While bodiless voices sob and sigh,
And shadows lurk by tree and stone
On Bala Lake.

Only the brave dare walk alone
Among the presences unseen
That haunt the lake on Hallowe'en.
Better to hear the monotone
Of troubled waters rolling by
Than seek to see, or wonder why,
Warned by the wind that rises high,
Old Aran trembles on her throne
On Hallowe'en.

Port Royal Tavern

(Jamaica.)

I've been on the Main with Morgan
Storming Porto Bello town,
And I've roamed the seas with Morgan
Where the Spanish ships go down:
He's a wise one and a wonder,
For when Morgan sails there's plunder,
It's a wild, roaring life is buccaneering.

Many leagues I've marched with Morgan
Over mountain, marsh and plain:
And if once you've sailed with Morgan
You'll be off with him again:
I've a sack of gems and money,
You can take your pick, my honey,
But I'll not wed and give up buccaneering.

I've been out with Henry Morgan
When the lads were dropping fast,
And the chances are with Morgan
Any trip can be your last:
But now I'm here, and warm with rum,
I see no sense in being glum,
Perhaps my turn will never come,
So kiss me lass, and drink to buccaneering.

A Day Which Endures Not

(Freely adapted from the Welsh of Elidr Sais, a 13th century poet.)

As for me
I have seen Llywelyn
With all the valiant men of Wales around him,
His armies like the hosts of Merfyn:
And have marched with chieftains mustering
From the northern hills
And the southern lowlands,
Pillars of war were they all, and mighty.

I have seen brave youth in battle
And heard the high thunder of horsemen:
I have drunk rare wines from chalices
Of silver, and have eaten rich repasts
Laid on fine linen
In the bountiful palaces of princes.

I have been among multitudes
And listened to much oratory;
To the chiming harmonies of bards
Declaiming their poems in intricate metres:
And have heard the songs and satires
Of itinerant minstrels,
And shared the merriment of men and women
Tickled by the saucy tales of story-tellers.

I have known festivals and ceremonies,
The gleam and the glitter of contests
Where strong men rejoiced in their prowess
And the clever in their cunning.

But now all these have gone
Like dreams in the dawning;
And thus must each man journey forth
In the hour of his calling
From a day which endures not.
In this, the lord of many lands,
The poor man's master,
Gains no reprieve,
No longer lease of life,
He passes through death's portal
With the peasant.

The Abbot of Abergavenny and the Pigs

The genial Abbot of Abergavenny
Sold thirty pigs for six pounds and a penny:
As these were bought by the Prior of York
The pigs were in for a pretty long walk.

The bargain was settled as C. O. D.,
Which is short for cash on delivery:
So the Abbot considered it proper and fair
To see for himself that the pigs got there.

He ordered his herdsman to blow a horn
Outside his window at early dawn,
To saddle the ponies, and get all set
For a quick start-off, whether dry or wet.

The morning was bright as they ambled out,
Each pig with a ring in its rooting snout,
And its feet protected with sandy tar
As was done to animals travelling far.

Dai the herdsman, a champion drover,
Took charge of the pigs, with Shôn and Rover,
His favourite couple of shepherd dogs
To head off the pigs from the woods and bogs.

The weather turned nasty as days went by,
And rain poured down from a dismal sky,
The fords were flooded, the winds grew rough,
And soon the going was terribly tough.

The farther they travelled the worse things got,
The Abbot said little, but thought a lot:
The ponies were weary, the dogs near done,
And only the pigs found the journey fun.

They squealed and frolicked and scampered away
As if they were out on a holiday,
Pelting through ditches and streams at the double,
Giving Dai and the dogs no end of trouble.

They chivied them here and they chased them there
Shouting and barking in grim despair,
Rounding them up and driving them on
Till tempers and patience were almost gone.

At night they found shelter in farms and barns
With Dai and the Abbot too tired for yarns:
So, with awful weather and pigs astray,
The journey lasted three weeks and a day.

Then just when they felt quite ready to drop
Dai heard the bells ring from the Minster top,
And, oh, how they rallied on hearing the din
Of the monks awaiting to welcome them in.

"Good gracious me," said the jovial Prior,
"How tired you look, hurry in to the fire,
And then as you're both so chilly and pale
We'll cheer you up with some Yorkshire ale."

Then he glanced at the pigs, and he sighed, "I say,
Why they've worn nearly half of their feet away:
Their trotters will hardly be nice to eat,
And most of the lot look to me dead-beat.

But if I know pigs, they will soon be fit:
And now you must stay with us for a bit,
Next week we will sample your famed Welsh pork
With our guests His Grace and the Mayor of York."

The Abbot, weary of pigs and their pranks,
Asked Dai to second his heartiest thanks:
So gladly they stopped for a rest in York,
Enjoying good company, food and talk.

At last came an end to their happy stay
And time to set out on their homeward way,
But both were disturbed by the same sad thought,
They hadn't been paid for the pigs they'd brought!

The courteous Abbot considered it brash
To mention the delicate matter of cash,
But Dai was more practical, "Sir," said he,
"About that money, just leave it to me."

Then off he went to the Prior's quarters,
And said, "Sir, what about all them porkers?
Though you've treated us grandly I'll not say no
If you'd like to settle before we go."

The Prior said, "Drat it," and "I be blowed,
I'd quite forgotten the debt I owed."
Then deep in his wallet he fumbled round
And carefully counted each separate pound.

But of smaller change he couldn't find any,
So he chuckled and said, "Well, I'll owe you the penny:"
Then Dai answered, "No Sir: I hope I'm not rude,
Please keep the odd cash, Sir, to help for our food."

Soon, the Prior and monks came trooping out
To say their goodbyes with a rousing shout:
And the Abbot and Dai shook hands en masse
And hoped that the bacon would prove first-class.

The sun was warm when they started away
And the ponies and dogs were spry and gay:
Said the Abbot to Dai when they'd ridden a mile,
"My friend, I've decided we'll travel in style.

Now that we're free of those pestilent pigs
I feel like dancing a couple of jigs,
And after surviving that awful trip north
We might as well both get our money's worth."

So they ambled at ease, enjoying the ride
Through the colourful scenes of the countryside,
Stopping at inns every evening to dine,
And now and then sharing a bottle of wine.

At night they each had a snug, warm bed,
And the dogs and ponies were so well fed
That when they got back to Abergavenny
They'd spent every bean and were down one penny.

Said the Abbot to Dai, "I'm sure that although
Our business has brought us no profit to show,
We'll think of this journey with pleasure and say
Now that was a jolly good holiday!"

Winter Day

(Freely adapted from a description by an unknown 11th century
Welsh poet.)

Fiercely falls the wind's flail
On wandering beast and wayfarer
Threshing the white hill barren:
There is no shelter here, no sanctuary
From the scourging blast
For homing men benighted.

The fords are fouled, the lake frozen,
Down there now in the furious hail
A gasping man, hard-spent, could pause
To ease his wheezing breath
By leaning on a single rigid reed.

Grey waves like great gaunt wolves
Leap at the groaning headlands:
And stumbling through the forest hoar-frost
The starved stag sinks and shudders.

Nothing moves in the numbed marshes
Where captive in the bleak, blue ice
And withered by the murderous weather
The sedge grows black and gangrened.

Nativity

(Poem for Christmas.)

Under the starry night,
Out in the silver weather,
Wrapped in their sheep-skins white
Shepherd-folk together ...
Telling tales of olden times,
And, while the clear moon climbs,
Hours pass like crystal chimes
(Talking together.)

Sudden beating of soft wings
(Michael, Raphael, Uriel)
Through the blue night that sings
Angel and Archangel
Bringing tidings strange to them ...
"Peace and good-will to men
Turn unto Bethlehem"
Gently spoke Gabriel.

Leaving their drowsy flocks
Straightway they turn and run
Over the shadowy rocks
Swiftly seeking—every one:
Warm in the straw's embrace
Child of the winsome face,
"Hail Mary full of grace,
We worship thy Son."

From the dim Caspian shore
Moving from well to well
(Caspar, Balthasar, Melchior)
With lutany and camel-bell:
Hear Mary sigh and sing
See her Baby smile and stir:
Gold, Frankincense and Myrrh ...
Treasures for the King.

For St. David's Day

Not with majestic pomp, nor with the sound
Of proud, imperial trumpets have we come
To this high heritage which is our home,
This Wales, this precious and enduring ground:
Not yet in unity, nor with one loud acclaim
Know we ourselves or our unfettered powers,
Divided from the fullness which is ours
Today as down those centuries of flame
When torn and pressed beyond our natural might
We failed and yielded in unequal fight.

Even so,
Beside the far-flung power whose strength we share,
We, ever in our essence separate,
Taking and giving freely, are aware
Of old traditions, streams of life which flow
From deep, abundant springs, within, below,
Up-welling from our racial memories:
And, crystalled to prophetic vision, these
Have hallowed all our inner sanctuaries
Where none may see, nor any walk among,
Save those who have the mystery of our tongue.
And so, while these remain, we, too, shall be
A nation and a people, doubly free,
Who through the passing of the centuries
Fulfil their own, their star-told destinies.

Branwen, the Wondrous Head and the Birds of Rhiannon

(Adapted from the Mabinogion story.)

Seven men escaped from the avenging strife
Which ravaged Ireland when Matholwch's wife,
The princess Branwen, Britain's loveliest maid
Was there, as Queen, dishonoured and betrayed.
With her they brought the head of Brân, their lord,
Who sorely wounded, bade them take a sword
And strike it from his body without fear,
For in their company for many a year
He promised, uncorrupted, to survive
In fellowship as warm as when alive:
Now Brân, fair Branwen's brother of renown
Was King of Britain, crowned in London town.

Ashore at Aber Alaw Branwen sighed
"O woe is me that I was born;" and cried
"Because of me two islands were made bare,
My son destroyed, and Brân beheaded there,"
So broken-hearted she lay down and died.
The Seven buried her on Alaw's side
In Talebolion, and then sadly sped
To Harlech with their King's commanding head:
Here he had ordered them to rest and stay
For seven years; to while the time away
With festive wine and meats, and song so rare
That nothing with that music could compare:
For there Rhiannon's birds along the sea
Sang thrilling them with their high ecstasy.

And so the Seven sat feasting, listening
To those three birds of wonder on the wing
Above the waters where the winds were stilled:
The waves with those sweet harmonies were filled
And changed to many colours, now flecked white,

Now hued with sapphire, then as dark as night,
Sparkling like diamonds, wan-smoked like pearl
Or glowing like a rosy-visaged girl:
Autumnal forests gave their tints untold,
And Summer corn that ripples into gold,
And lilac wreathed about with purple mist
Beryl and ruby, jade and amethyst.

The glories of the rainbow swiftly came,
Soft moved the waves with April in green flame,
Then gay with June, now glossy as the larch,
Then foam-white with the torrent strength of March:
The sea to such bright melody was won
It heeded not the passing of the sun.

The Seven were often silent, marvelling
At so occult and magical a thing:
And their appointed years went quickly by
With bird-song over earth and sea and sky,
Until at last they looked and saw afar
Rhiannon's birds, each like a singing star,
Fade into darkness. Then with lips unsealed
Each spoke of secrets that the songs revealed,
And hastening through the twilight of the trees
They took their ship and sought the Penfro seas.

They came to Grassholm with the Wondrous Head
And lived in joy till four score years had fled,
Forgetting every sorrow they had known,
And unaware so long a time had flown,
For Brân remained their counsellor and friend
Through those delightful years. But in the end
An act of disobedience broke the spell
Of their companionship, and ruin fell
Upon their happiness because one day
Impetuous Heilyn dared to disobey
His lord's command, and opened wide the door
That looked towards the distant Cornish shore,
Through which Brân had forbidden them to pry,
Knowing that when this happened he would die.

And then, at once, their ancient grief returned
More poignantly than ever; their hearts burned
With anguish for their kinsmen who were slain,
And memories of misfortune came again:
Most bitter blow of all, the Wondrous Head
Took on corruption and great Brân was dead.
And from that moment none of them could rest,
So starting on their journey from the West
According to their lord's command they bore
His head to London where long years before
He had been crowned, and buried it at night
In deep concealment in the Mount called White.
Such power remained within the Wondrous Head
Facing the realm of France, that it was said
No plague could cross the sea to Britain's ground
Unless its hidden burial place was found.
And so, the head as Warden of the sea,
For years from pestilence kept Britain free.

The Black Pagans

(The Viking Invaders of Wales.)

Ten score tongues could not tell
The tale of their fell coming:
How swiftly in these dark, disastrous days
The dragon-headed longships spawned
Their ruthless hosts of fierce sea-rovers
Upon defenceless coasts
In the blown spume of their spurting prows,
Proudly riding the high tides running
Over the moaning river-mouths,
And cheating the treacherous silting sands
With skilled seafarers' cunning.

And then, like ravenous wolves
Hungry for prey, they prowled
From their landfall lair
Lusting for plunder, and sacked
The peaceful places of prayer,
Cleaving down and asunder
The cloistered servants of Christ,
Defiling the shrines, despoiling the altars:
Swinging their great axe-blades,
Unleashing the terror of torches
On their pitiless raids, they scattered abroad
The sacred relics of saints, and shattered
The yew-wrought caskets, the cherished
Reliquaries of quiet churches
That perished in flame and were gone,
With statues sculptured in stone
And carvings of crosses and Calvaries,
And the luminous treasures that shone
In breviaries, missals and manuscripts:
Barbarians blind with murderous rage
Destroying the precious and rare things made

From year to year and age to age
With blade and chisel and brush and pen
For the praise and the greater glory of God
By the hands of inspired craftsmen.
And falling with fury on hamlet and homestead
They wrecked the deep wells, the fish-ponds, the mills,
And the murmuring domes of the dove-cots,
Turning the dwellings of chieftains and peasants,
Their barns and their byres,
Into fires that blazed through the night
With their burning.
Below the high rocks of the hills
They filled the lone sheep-folds
With the soft slain of the slaughtered flocks,
And killed the cattle on the lowland plain
For their gluttonous feasting:
Warriors holding roaring wassail
In the ravished palaces of princes,
And uttering uncouth oaths
In the eloquent places of poetry:
They slew the bards at their song
Brutally, their blood-gouts glowed like berries
In the ruined halls of their lords' houses:
Their bodies lie huddled in grievous shambles
Of shameful graves
Enshrouded by briars and brambles.

But the spoils of silver and gold,
Chalices, patens and croziers,
Hallowed and honoured of old,
Bright tapestries, vestments and robes
Embellished with art, and refined
Into beauty of glowing embroidery,
Brooches and bracelets of bronze
And beads of carnelian and amber,
With ornaments richly designed
In devices of delicate metal,
Tunics, cuirasses and torques,

Ivory chess-boards and chess-men,
And the fleetest of falcons and hawks
They carried away to their ships:
And harried from many a hamlet's graves
The weeping young they seized as slaves
For sale in the pagan world,
The strong-limbed, virile youths of the vales
And the comeliest, nubile girls.

And now there is no comforter at hand,
No priest, no pilgrim and no gracious lord,
Nor bard nor harpist
Within these leagues of devastated land:
This golden oratory of poets and minstrels
Is broken utterly and blackened:
And we who live bereaved, alone,
In fear and barren plight
Hear only the keening threnody
Of the wind of the dead at night
In the dark, in the loud winter:
There is no other melody or song
But our remembered litany
Murmured to save us from the heathen sword,
"From the wild fury of the Northmen
Deliver us, good Lord;"
We have known death and desolation
For so long
That ten score tongues could not tell of it.